ROCK & POP

G

ROCK & POP

TRINITY
COLLEGE LONDON

THE EXAM
AT A GLANCE

For your Rock & Pop exam you will need to perform a set of **three songs** and one of the **Session skills** assessments, either **Playback** or **Improvising**. You can choose the order in which you play your set-list.

Song 1

Choose a song from this book

OR from www.trinityrock.com

Song 2

Choose a different song from this book

OR from www.trinityrock.com

OR perform a song you have chosen yourself: this could be your own cover version or a song you have written. It should be at the same level as the songs in this book. See the website for detailed requirements.

Song 3: Technical focus

Choose one of the Technical focus songs from this book, which cover three specific technical elements.

Session skills

Choose either **Playback** or **Improvising**.

When you are preparing for your exam please check on **www.trinityrock.com** for the most up-to-date information and requirements as these can change from time to time.

CONTENTS

Tuning track: E, A, D, G, B, E with a pause between each note.

Trinity College London's Rock & Pop syllabus and supporting publications have been devised and produced in association with Faber Music and Peters Edition London.

Trinity College London
Registered office:
89 Albert Embankment
London SE1 7TP UK
T + 44 (0)20 7820 6100
F + 44 (0)20 7820 6161
E music@trinitycollege.co.uk
www.trinitycollege.co.uk

Registered in the UK. Company no. 02683033
Charity no. 1014792
Patron HRH The Duke of Kent KG

Copyright © 2012 Trinity College London
First published in 2012 by Trinity College London

Third impression, January 2013

Cover and book design by Chloë Alexander
Brand development by Andy Ashburner @ Caffeinehit (www.caffeinehit.com)
Photographs courtesy of Rex Features Limited.
Printed in England by Caligraving Ltd

Audio produced, mixed and mastered by Tom Fleming
Guitar arranged by Tom Fleming
Backing tracks arranged by Tom Fleming
Musicians
Vocals: Bo Walton, Brendan Reilly & Alison Symons
Keyboards: Oliver Weeks
Guitar: Tom Fleming
Bass: Ben Hillyard
Drums: George Double
Studio Engineer: Joel Davies www.thelimehouse.com

ISBN: 978-0-85736-221-6

SONGS SUNSHINE OF YOUR LOVE

Cream

Words and Music by Jack Bruce, Peter Brown and Eric Clapton

♩ = 116 **Blues Rock**   *2 bars count-in*

© 1967 Dratleaf Ltd and E C Music
Warner/Chappell Music Ltd and E C Music

www.trinityrock.com

SONGS TURN! TURN! TURN!

The Byrds
Words: Book Of Ecclesiastes, Adaption and Music by Pete Seeger

♩ = 140 **Folk Pop** *2 bars count-in*

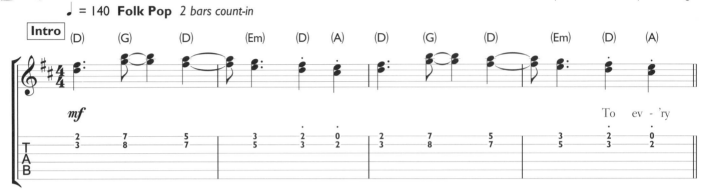

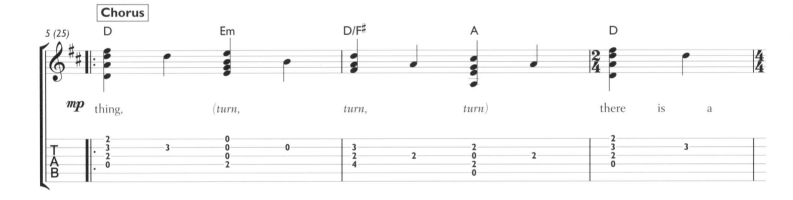

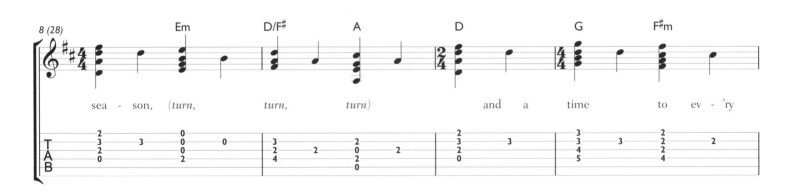

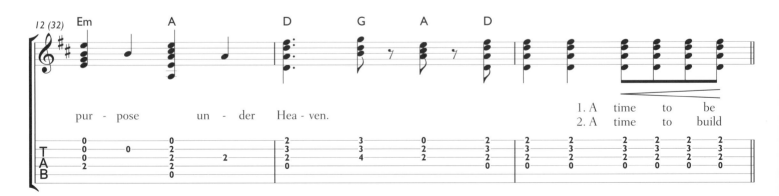

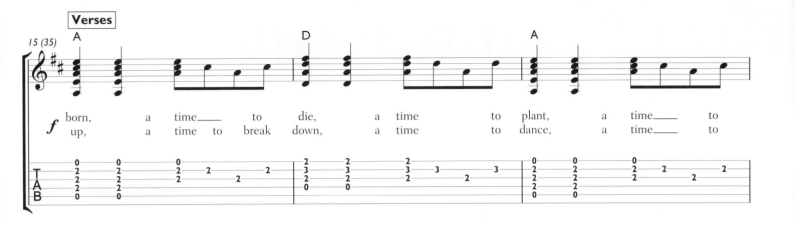

Verses

15 (35)

born, a time_____ to die, a time to plant, a time_____ to
up, a time to break down, a time to dance, a time_____ to

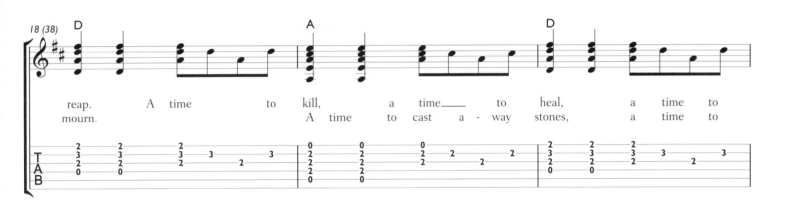

18 (38)

reap. A time to kill, a time_____ to heal, a time to
mourn. A time to cast a - way stones, a time to

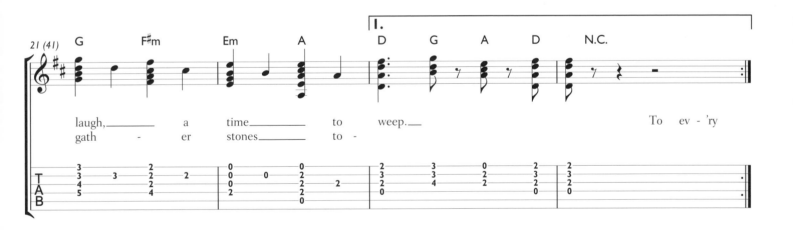

21 (41)

laugh,_____ a time_____ to weep._____ To ev - 'ry
gath - er stones_____ to -

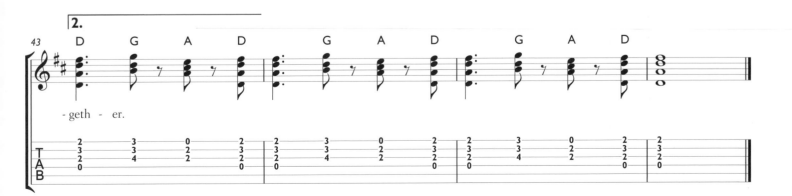

43

- geth - er.

SONGS ALL DAY AND ALL OF THE NIGHT

The Kinks
Words and Music by Ray Davies

♩ = 136 **Rock** *2 bars count-in*

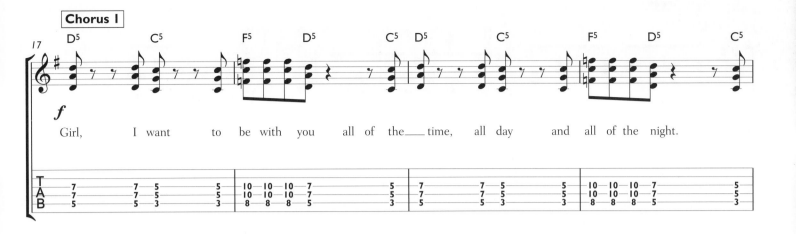

Girl, I want to be with you all of the ___ time, all day and all of the night.

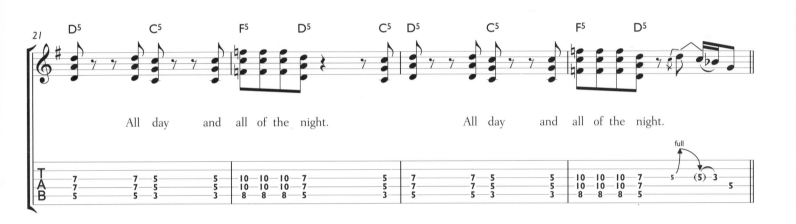

All day and all of the night. All day and all of the night.

Guitar solo

Bass break

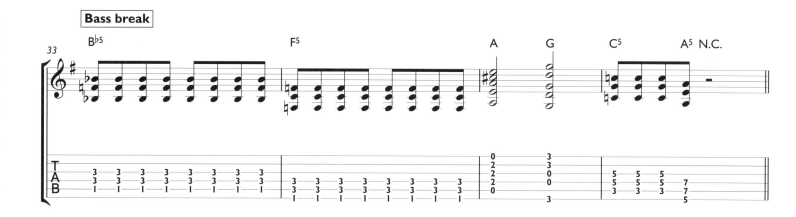

Chorus 2

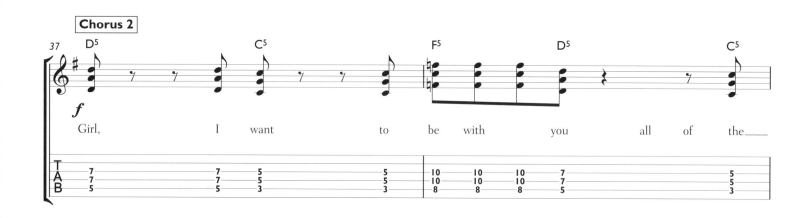

Girl, I want to be with you all of the____

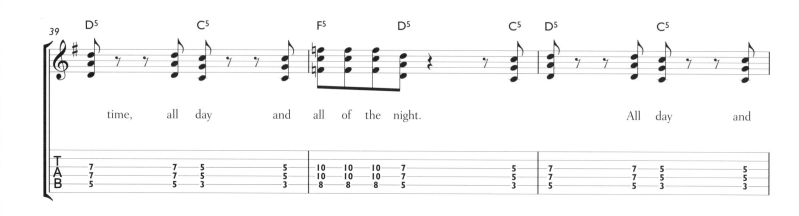

time, all day and all of the night. All day and

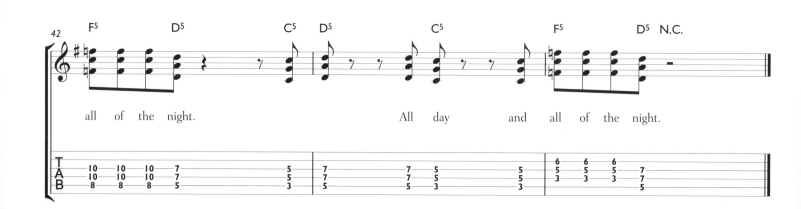

all of the night. All day and all of the night.

SONGS JOHN BARLEYCORN

Traditional
Words and Music Trad.

♩ = 90 **Folk** *2 bars count-in*

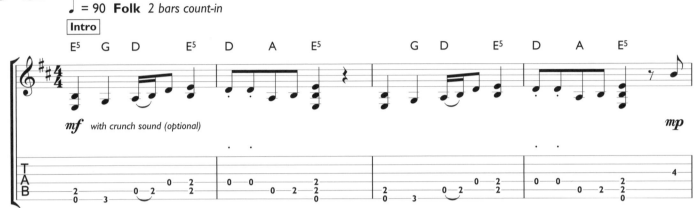

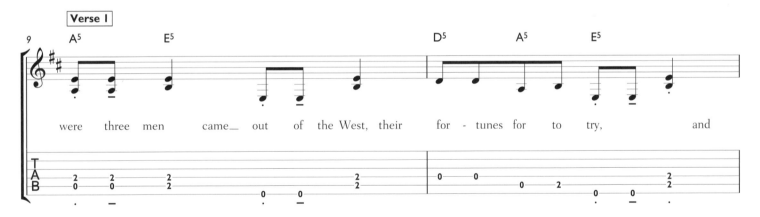

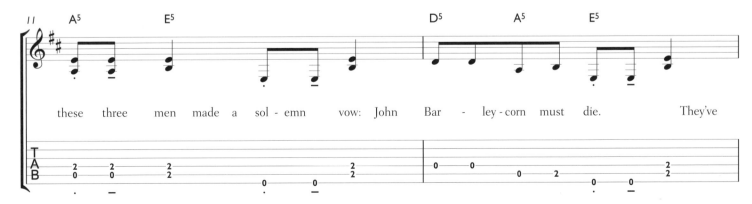

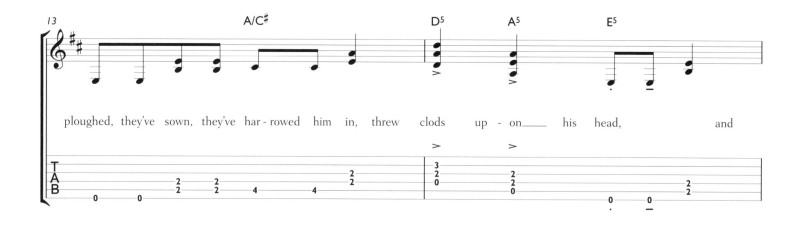

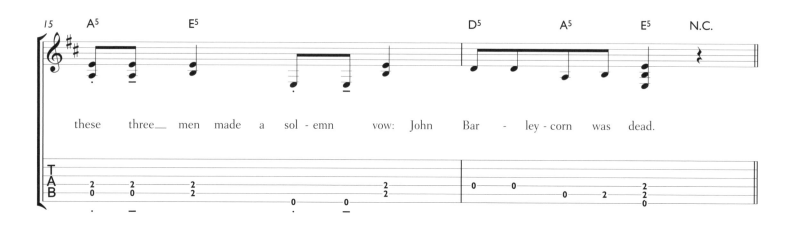

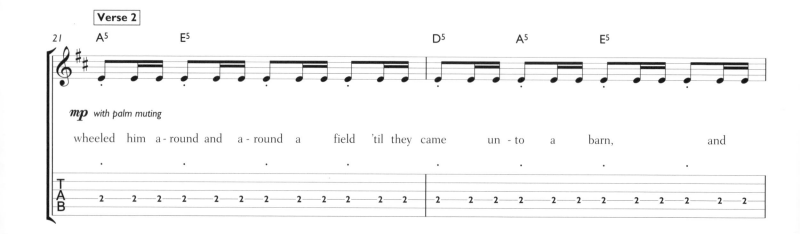

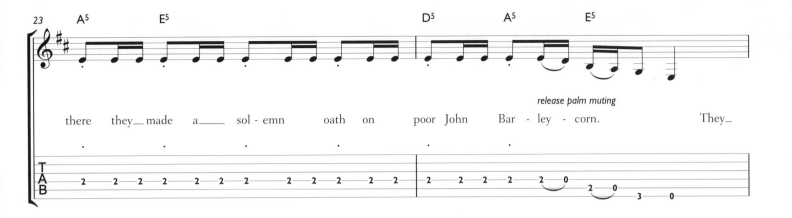

there they_ made a__ sol-emn oath on poor John Bar-ley-corn. They_

release palm muting

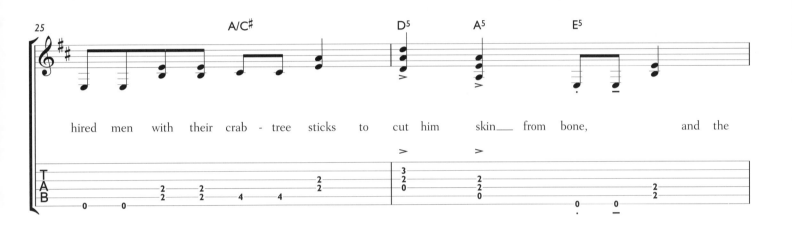

hired men with their crab-tree sticks to cut him skin__ from bone, and the

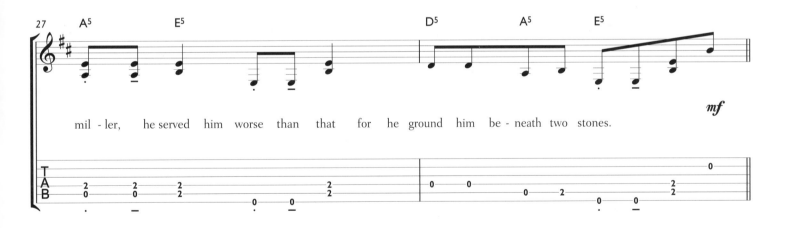

mil-ler, he served him worse than that for he ground him be-neath two stones.

Outro

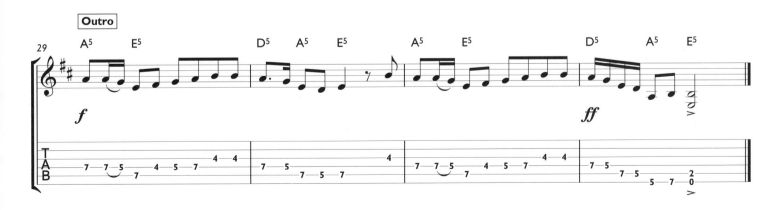

YOUR PAGE NOTES

CREEP

In your exam, you will be assessed on the following technical elements:

1 Arpeggiated chords

The chords in the verse should be arpeggiated (with plectrum) and allowed to ring as much as possible.

2 Dynamic range

'Creep' uses extreme dynamics to reflect the words. The song opens relatively calmly and *mp*, which stands for *mezzo piano* and means moderately quiet. The mood changes dramatically towards the end of the verse as it builds up to the words 'But I'm a creep'. The dynamic marking here is *f* (*forte* = loud). The song ends *pp*, which stands for *pianissimo* and means very quiet. Make sure that the contrasts between these dynamics can be heard.

3 Guitar sounds

There are two different guitar sounds in this song: one for the verse and another for the chorus. These sounds should be balanced so that the distortion is a little louder than the clean sound. Both need to be balanced against the other instruments and the vocals on the CD – take care not to drown them.

The percussive muted chords leading into the chorus should be played very aggressively, aiming for an effect a bit like a gunshot.

CREEP

TRACK 10 demo
TRACK 11 backing

Radiohead
Words and Music by Thomas Yorke, Jonathan Greenwood, Colin Greenwood, Edward O'Brien, Philip Selway, Albert Hammond and Mike Hazelwood

♩ = 96 **Indie Ballad** *2 bars count-in*

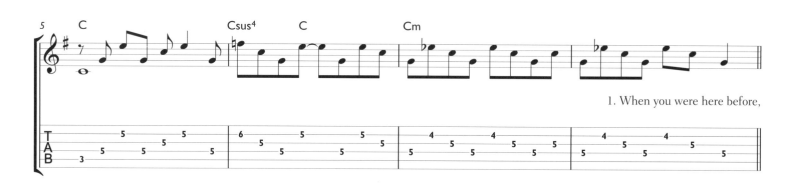

1. When you were here before,

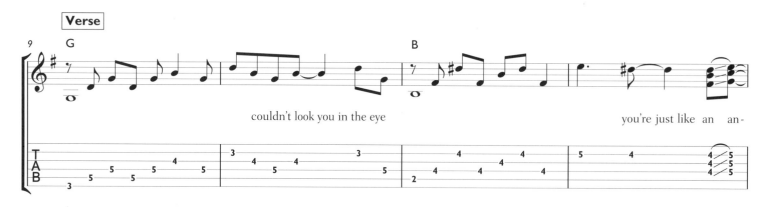

couldn't look you in the eye   you're just like an an-

- gel,   your skin makes me   cry.___   You float like a fea-

-ther,_____ in a beautiful world. I wish I was spe-

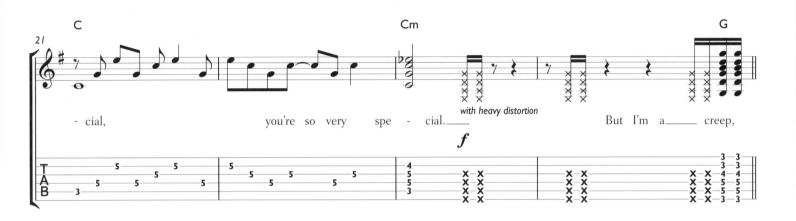

-cial, you're so very spe - cial.____ *with heavy distortion* But I'm a___ creep,

f

Chorus

I'm a___ weird - o._____ What the hell__ am I do-ing here?

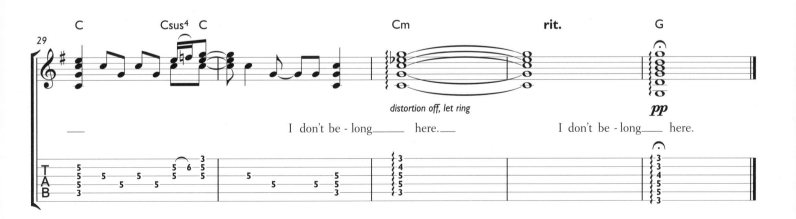

distortion off, let ring

rit.

I don't be - long_____ here.____ I don't be - long___ here.

pp

BASKET CASE

In your exam, you will be assessed on the following technical elements:

1 Down-strokes

For maximum authenticity, down-strokes should be used for the repeated ♩♪♪♪ ♪♪♪♩ on the first two pages of this song. Make sure that these notes are played evenly and energetically but strictly in time. Practise slowly at first, then gradually build up the speed as you become more confident.

2 Accents

The accents are an important element of the style of this song. They come on different beats of the bar; some bars have two accents while others have three. Be ready for these and be sure that the accented notes are louder than the others. Palm muting should be used and released on the accents.

3 Power chords

This song is almost entirely made up of power chords. There are a few major chords later in the song: these are essentially power chords and the top note may be omitted, particularly if using heavy distortion.

When playing power chords on the bottom strings, especially at this speed, take care not to strike open treble strings accidentally.

BASKET CASE

TRACK 12 demo TRACK 13 backing

Green Day

Words and Music by Billie Joe Armstrong, Frank E. Wright III and Michael Pritchard

♩ = 168 **Fast Rock** *2 bars count-in*

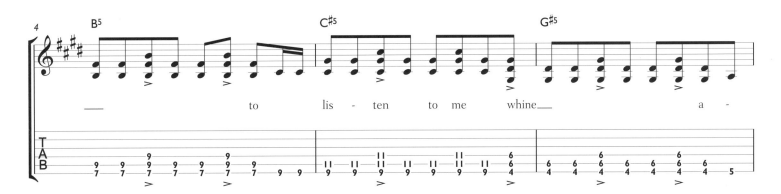

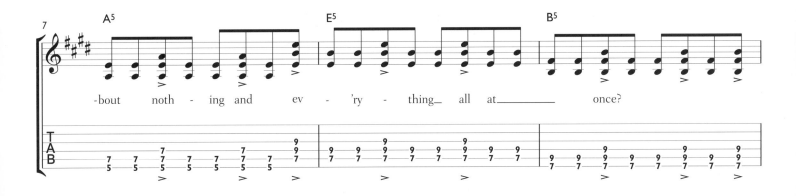

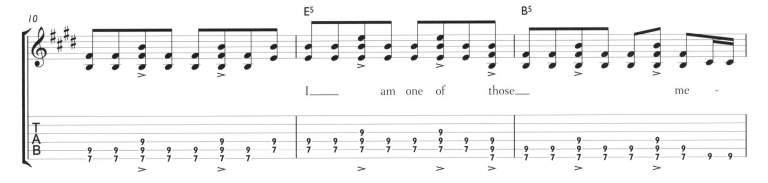

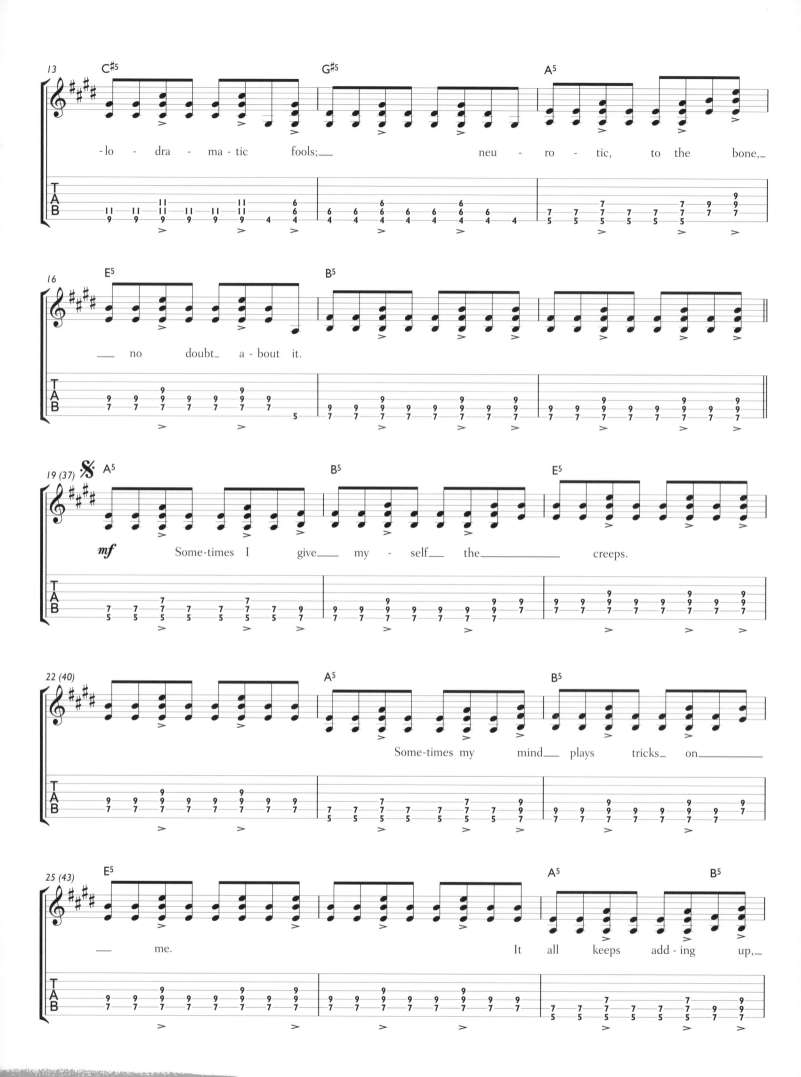

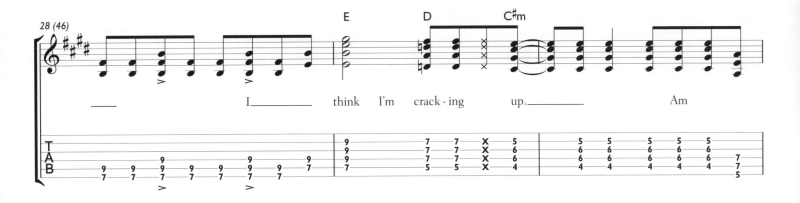

I _____ think I'm crack - ing up. _____ Am

I just ____ pa - ra - noid? ____ Ah yeah, yeah, yeah.

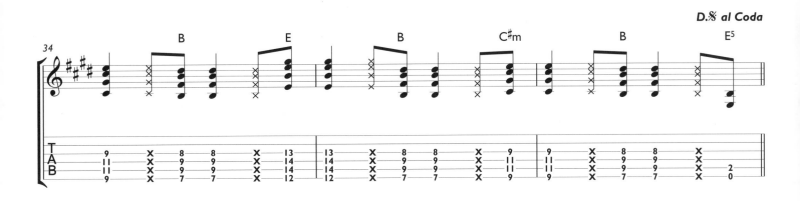

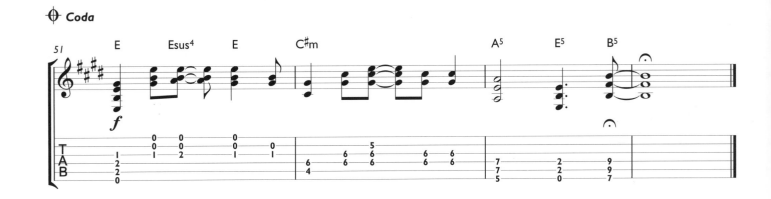

SUNSHINE OF YOUR LOVE

Cream

'Sunshine Of Your Love' is one of several classic songs on Cream's highly influential blues-rock album *Disraeli Gears* (1967). The band comprised Eric Clapton (guitar), Jack Bruce (bass) and Ginger Baker (drums) – each of them highly accomplished rock musicians, coming together as probably the first rock supergroup. They started as a blues revival band but their style gradually evolved into hard rock. They were famous for their live performances and long improvised solos.

'Sunshine Of Your Love' opens with one of the most famous riffs ever recorded.

The intro and verse of 'Sunshine Of Your Love' feature a descending guitar riff using the blues scale. This riff is doubled by the bass guitar: listen to the bass and make sure that you are exactly in time with it. The second half of the figure is syncopated, with each note falling on the off-beat. These off-beat notes should all be played with up-strokes – but take care not to rush.

The chorus uses heavy chords which are played in the same rhythm as the bass part. Although major chords are written here, these are essentially power chords and the major third (on the highest string in each shape) may be omitted – particularly if using a distortion sound, which makes major chords sound muddy.

The guitar solo (bars 29–36) uses bends. These should generally be played in tune, although this can be relaxed slightly in this blues context.

This song is also in the bass and drums books, so you can get together and play it in a band.

'I'll *be* with *you* when *the* stars start *falling*'

TURN! TURN! TURN!

The Byrds

The Byrds were a very successful American band during the 1960s and 1970s. They were pioneers of folk-rock – a style of music combining elements of American country folk and rock music. Their distinctive sound was marked by melodic vocal harmonies and the instantly recognisable sound of Roger McGuinn's 12-string guitar.

'Turn! Turn! Turn!' is the title track of The Byrds' 1965 album. It was originally written by Pete Seeger, who took the lyrics, almost verbatim from the biblical Book of Ecclesiastes. The song, which was released during the Vietnam war, pleas for peace: this struck a chord with the American public of the time.

PERFORMANCE · HINTS & TIPS ·

The intro to 'Turn! Turn! Turn!' uses double-stopped thirds on the top E and B strings. These should be played as cleanly and clearly as possible. Make sure that the timing is accurate and take care not to rush the syncopated notes.

After the intro, the guitar accompanies the vocal line using simple chords: use a 'let ring' effect on each.

'Turn! Turn! Turn!' is in $\frac{4}{4}$, but be ready for the change to $\frac{2}{4}$ at bars 7 and 10.

'A *time* to *ev'ry* purpose *under* Heaven'

ALL DAY AND ALL OF THE NIGHT

The Kinks

The Kinks were one of the most influential bands of the 1960s. A four-piece London Mod band, they produced short punchy songs, often with high quality lyrics written by their singer Ray Davies. Like many British bands of that time, they began as an R&B group but their style changed over their long career.

The Kinks had a string of hit singles during the 1960s, including 'All Day And All Of The Night', which is built upon a simple sliding power chord riff.

PERFORMANCE HINTS & TIPS

Most of this song uses three-note power chords moving in parallel. Move these as quickly and smoothly as possible, although part of the character of the riff comes from the fact that some slides will always be audible. Play the riff with down-strokes only.

The short solo at bar 25 uses the G minor pentatonic scale in third position. The bend in bar 26 does not necessarily have to reach the exact target note (D): an authentic bluesy effect will be achieved by a slightly flat bend.

The double-stopped notes in the solo should be played by flattening the first finger across the G and B strings at the third fret.

This song is also in the vocals, keyboards, bass and drums books, so you can get together and play it in a band.

'Girl, *I want* to be *with* you. *all of* the *time*'

JOHN BARLEYCORN

Traffic

'John Barleycorn' is an English folk ballad with a long history dating back to the 16th century. This song – like all songs in the ballad tradition – tells a story. Nobody is really sure who John Barleycorn was, but one idea is that the name represents alcoholic drinks made from barley – a type of corn. There have been many versions of this song, by both folk singers and rock musicians. The 1960s rock band Traffic even named one of their best-selling albums after it – *John Barleycorn Must Die*.

• PERFORMANCE • HINTS & TIPS •

'John Barleycorn' should sound like a folk dance. Make sure that you follow all the articulation markings. Some notes in the intro are marked with slurs – play these as smoothly as you can. The other notes should be more separated.

Verse 2 contains a passage of repeated ♪♫ notes. The first of each group is marked *staccato*: make sure that they are played short and light.

The ♪♩ marked *staccato* followed by *tenuto* (in, for example, bar 9) should be played using right-hand palm muting for the first note, which should be released for the second.

The amp may be set to a clean or slight crunch sound for this song: either way it is important to set the amp volume sufficiently loud so that the printed dynamics can be produced.

This song is also in the vocals, keyboards, bass and drums books, so you can get together and play it in a band.

'These *three* men *made* a solemn vow'

CREEP

Radiohead

'Creep' was a surprise worldwide hit for Radiohead in 1993. It was originally released as a single and then again on Radiohead's early album *Pablo Honey*. The self-loathing lyrics tell of an unsuccessful crush – hitting an angst-ridden nerve that clearly many can identify with.

The song opens with Thom Yorke's vulnerable-sounding voice against a sparse background of guitar and drums. This quiet, restrained opening builds up through a long *crescendo* to a climax with wailing falsetto and distorted guitars, falling back down again to the bittersweet plaintive sounds of the opening.

The mood of 'Creep' changes dramatically as it progresses. It opens in a relatively calm, quiet mood, with arpeggiated chords. Then, as the words become angrier towards the end of the verse, the music gets louder and more aggressive, with full, distorted chords. The song ends very quietly – to reflect the mood of sad resignation.

Use a distortion pedal or a two-channel amp with footswitch to switch between the clean sound required for the verse and the heavy distortion in the chorus.

This song is also in the drums book, so you can play it together.

'I *don't* belong *here*'

www.trinityrock.com

BASKET CASE

Green Day

Green Day is a three-piece Californian pop punk band – Billie Joe Armstrong (vocals and guitar), Mike Dirnt (bass and backing vocals) and Tre Cool (drums). 'Basket Case' is taken from Green Day's 1994 album *Dookie* which is heavily rooted in American punk. Green Day was widely credited with popularising and reviving punk rock in the United States. The lyrics of 'Basket Case' were inspired by Armstrong's personal experience of panic attacks.

PERFORMANCE · HINTS & TIPS

'Basket Case' is a very fast and energetic song. The main challenge with this guitar part is to maintain the energy and keep the timing accurate – despite the fast tempo.

The symbol at the end of bar 36 means *Dal Segno* (from the sign) and then to the Coda. When you reach the **D.% al Coda** in bar 36 you go back to the % sign (in bar 19) and play this passage again until you reach 'To Coda' at bar 32. You then jump to where it says 'Coda' to finish the song.

There is a pause on the final note: be sure that you hold this on longer than its normal value.

'Am *I* just *paranoid?* Ah yeah, yeah, *yeah*'

PLAYBACK

For your exam, you can choose either Playback or Improvising (see page 30).
If you choose Playback, you will be asked to play some music you have not seen
or heard before.

In the exam, you will be given the song chart and the examiner will play a recording
of the music. You will hear several two-bar or four-bar phrases on the recording:
you should play each of them straight back in turn. There's a rhythm track going
throughout, which helps you keep in time. There should not be any gaps in the music.

In the exam you will have two chances to play with the recording:
- First time – for practice
- Second time – for assessment.

You should listen to the audio, copying what you hear; you can also read the music.
Here are some practice song charts which are also on the CD in this book.

Don't forget that the Playback test can include requirements which may not be
shown in these examples, including those from earlier grades. Check the parameters
at www.trinityrock.com to prepare for everything which might come up in your exam.

Practice playback 1

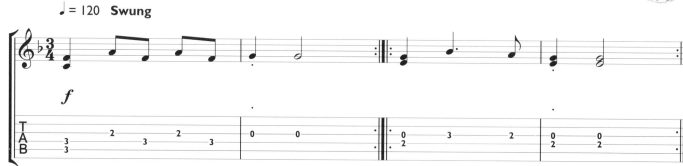

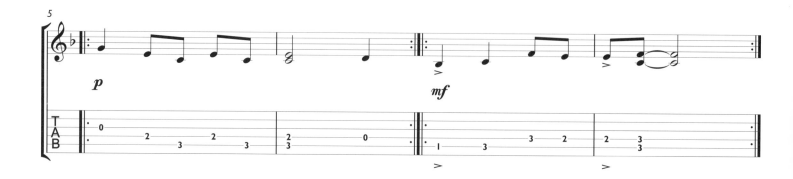

Practice playback 2

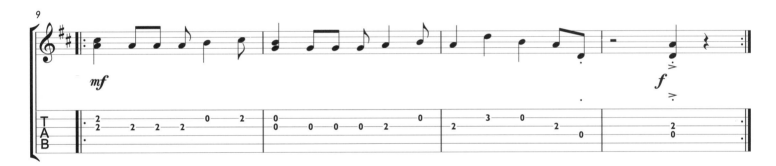

'I really *like*
the *way*
music *looks* on *paper.*
It *looks* like *art*
to *me*'

Steve Vai

SESSION SKILLS

IMPROVISING

For your exam, you can choose either Playback (see page 28), or Improvising. If you choose to improvise, you will be asked to improvise over a backing track that you haven't heard before in a specified style.

In the exam, you will be given a song chart and the examiner will play a recording of the backing track. The backing track consists of a passage of music played on a loop. You can choose whether to play a lead melodic line, rhythmic chords, or a combination of the two.

In the exam you will have two chances to play with the recording:
- First time – for practice
- Second time – for assessment.

Here are some improvising charts for practice which are also on the CD in this book.

Don't forget that the Improvising test can include requirements which may not be shown in these examples, including those from earlier grades. Check the parameters at www.trinityrock.com to prepare for everything which might come up in your exam.

Practice improvisation 1

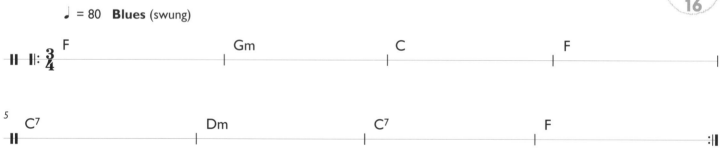

♩ = 80 **Blues** (swung)

| F | Gm | C | F |
| C⁷ | Dm | C⁷ | F |

Practice improvisation 2

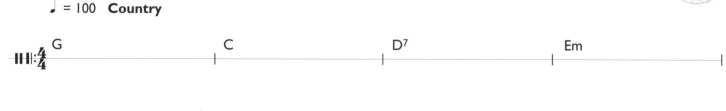

♩ = 100 **Country**

| G | C | D⁷ | Em |
| Bm | Am | C | G |

CHOOSING A SONG FOR YOUR EXAM

There are lots of options to help you choose your three songs for the exam. For Songs 1 and 2, you can choose a song which is:

- from this book
- from www.trinityrock.com

Or for Song 2 you can choose a song which is:

- sheet music from a printed or online source
- your own arrangement of a song or a song you have written yourself (see page 32).

You can play the song unaccompanied or with a backing track (minus the guitar part). If you like, you can create a backing track yourself (or with friends), or you could add your own vocals – or both.

For Grade 3, the song should last between one-and-a-half and three-and-a-half minutes, and the level of difficulty should be similar to your other songs. When choosing a song, think about:

- Does it work on my instrument?
- Are there any technical elements that are too difficult for me? (If so, perhaps save it for when you do the next grade.)
- Do I enjoy playing it?
- Does it work with my other pieces to create a good set-list?

See www.trinityrock.com for further information and advice on choosing your own song.

SHEET MUSIC

You must always bring an original copy of the book or a download sheet with email certificate for each song you perform in the exam. If you choose to write your own song you must provide the examiner with a copy of the sheet music. Your music can be:

- a lead sheet with lyrics, chords and melody line
- a chord chart with lyrics
- a full score using conventional staff notation
- see page 32 for details on presenting a song you have written yourself.

The title of the song and your name should be on the sheet music.

WRITING YOUR OWN SONG

You can play a song that you have written yourself for one of the choices in your exam. For Grade 3, your song should last between one-and-a-half and three-and-a-half minutes. It is sometimes difficult to know where to begin, however. Here are some suggestions for starting points:

- **A rhythm**: A short repeated rhythm will often underpin an entire song. Start by writing a couple of short rhythms here:

- **A riff**: A riff is a short rhythm which is repeated over and over. A short repeated riff will often underpin an entire song. Write a couple of riffs here:

WRITING YOUR SONG DOWN

Rock and pop music is often written as a **lead sheet** with the lyrics (if there are any), chords and a melody line.

- As a guitar player, you may want to write your part on a **five-line stave** or as **tab**. Both have been used for the songs in this book.

- You can, if you prefer, use a **graph** or **table** to represent your music, as long as it is clear to anyone else (including the examiner) how the song goes.

- **Instruments**: Which instruments will play your song? You could just use solo guitar, or you could add your own vocals and include other instruments.

There are plenty of other ways of starting: perhaps with a melody, chord sequence or a lyric, for example.

You will also need to consider the **structure** of your song (verse and chorus, 12-bar blues, and so on), the **style** it is in (blues, hard rock, etc.).

There are many choices to be made – which is why writing a song is such a rewarding thing to do.

PLAYING IN A BAND

Playing in a band is exciting: it can be a lot of fun and, as with everything, the more you do it, the easier it gets. It is very different from playing on your own. Everyone contributes to the overall sound: the most important skill you need to develop is listening.

For a band to sound good, the players need to be 'together' – that mainly means keeping in time with each other, but also playing at the same volume, and with the same kind of feeling.

Your relationship with the other band members is also important. Talk with them about the music you play, the music you like, and what you'd like the band to achieve short-term and long-term.

Band rehearsals are important – you should not be late, tired or distracted by your mobile phone! Being positive makes a huge difference. Try to create a friendly atmosphere in rehearsals so that everybody feels comfortable trying out new things. Don't worry about making mistakes: that is what rehearsals are for.

'All Day And All Of The Night' (page 8) and 'John Barleycorn' (page 11) are arranged for band. You will find parts for vocals, keyboards, bass and drums in the other Trinity Rock & Pop Grade 3 books or available online. There are also parts for 'Sunshine Of Your Love' in Trinity Rock & Pop Grade 3 Bass and Drums books. Trinity offers exams for groups of musicians at various levels. The songs arranged for bands are ideal to include as part of a song-list for these exams. Have a look at the website for more details.

HINTS AND TIPS

- Your own ability as a musician is important – if you have practised different techniques on your own, then you will have more to offer to the band. It is worth remembering that simple parts can be very effective, it is not always necessary for each instrument to play every note in the chord, or on every beat of the bar.

- If you have two guitars, try and make the sound of each guitar different. It can sound clearer if the guitars play different parts or in different styles.

- Some instruments could stop playing in certain sections. This is a very effective way of increasing the range of dynamics.

PLAYING WITH BACKING TRACKS

The CD contains demos and backing tracks of all the songs in the book. The additional songs at www.trinityrock.com also come with demos and backing tracks.

- In your exam, you should perform with the backing track, or you can create your own (see below).
- The backing tracks begin with a click track, which sets the tempo and helps you start accurately.
- Be careful to set the balance between the volume of the backing track and your instrument.
- Listen carefully to the backing track to ensure you are playing in time.

If you are creating your own backing track here are some further tips:
- Make sure the sound quality is of a good standard.
- Think carefully about the instruments/sounds you are putting on the backing track.
- Avoid copying what you are playing on the backing track – it should support not duplicate.
- Do you need to include a click track at the beginning?

COPYRIGHT IN A SONG

If you are a singer or songwriter it is important to know about copyright. When someone writes a song or creates an arrangement they own the copyright (sometimes called 'the rights') to that version. The copyright means that other people cannot copy it, sell it, perform it in a concert, make it available online or record it without the owner's permission or the appropriate licence. When you write a song you automatically own the copyright to it, which means that other people cannot copy your work. But just as importantly, you cannot copy other people's work, or perform it in public without their permission or the appropriate licence.

Points to remember
- You can create a cover version of a song for an exam or other non-public performance.
- You cannot record your cover version and make your recording available to others (by copying it or uploading it to a website) without the appropriate licence.
- You own the copyright of your own original song, which means that no one is allowed to copy it.
- You cannot copy someone else's song without their permission or the appropriate licence.
- If you would like to use somebody else's words in your own song you must check if they are in copyright and, if so, we recommend you confirm with the author that they are happy for the words to be used as lyrics.
- Materials protected by copyright can normally be used as lyrics in our examinations as these are private performances under copyright law. The examiner may ask you the name of the original author in the exam.
- When you present your own song to the examiner, make sure you include the title, the names of any writers and the source of your lyrics.

YOUR PAGE

NOTES

ALSO AVAILABLE

Trinity College London Rock & Pop examinations 2012-2017 are also available for:

Bass Initial
ISBN: 978-0-85736-227-8

Bass Grade 1
ISBN: 978-0-85736-228-5

Bass Grade 2
ISBN: 978-0-85736-229-2

Bass Grade 3
ISBN: 978-0-85736-230-8

Bass Grade 4
ISBN: 978-0-85736-231-5

Bass Grade 5
ISBN: 978-0-85736-232-2

Bass Grade 6
ISBN: 978-0-85736-233-9

Bass Grade 7
ISBN: 978-0-85736-234-6

Bass Grade 8
ISBN: 978-0-85736-235-3

Drums Initial
ISBN: 978-0-85736-245-2

Drums Grade 1
ISBN: 978-0-85736-246-9

Drums Grade 2
ISBN: 978-0-85736-247-6

Drums Grade 3
ISBN: 978-0-85736-248-3

Drums Grade 4
ISBN: 978-0-85736-249-0

Drums Grade 5
ISBN: 978-0-85736-250-6

Drums Grade 6
ISBN: 978-0-85736-251-3

Drums Grade 7
ISBN: 978-0-85736-252-0

Drums Grade 8
ISBN: 978-0-85736-253-7

Guitar Initial
ISBN: 978-0-85736-218-6

Guitar Grade 1
ISBN: 978-0-85736-219-3

Guitar Grade 2
ISBN: 978-0-85736-220-9

Guitar Grade 3
ISBN: 978-0-85736-221-6

Guitar Grade 4
ISBN: 978-0-85736-222-3

Guitar Grade 5
ISBN: 978-0-85736-223-0

Guitar Grade 6
ISBN: 978-0-85736-224-7

Guitar Grade 7
ISBN: 978-0-85736-225-4

Guitar Grade 8
ISBN: 978-0-85736-226-1

Keyboards Initial
ISBN: 978-0-85736-236-0

Keyboards Grade 1
ISBN: 978-0-85736-237-7

Keyboards Grade 2
ISBN: 978-0-85736-238-4

Keyboards Grade 3
ISBN: 978-0-85736-239-1

Keyboards Grade 4
ISBN: 978-0-85736-240-7

Keyboards Grade 5
ISBN: 978-0-85736-241-4

Keyboards Grade 6
ISBN: 978-0-85736-242-1

Keyboards Grade 7
ISBN: 978-0-85736-243-8

Keyboards Grade 8
ISBN: 978-0-85736-244-5

Vocals Initial
ISBN: 978-0-85736-254-4

Vocals Grade 1
ISBN: 978-0-85736-255-1

Vocals Grade 2
ISBN: 978-0-85736-256-8

Vocals Grade 3
ISBN: 978-0-85736-257-5

Vocals Grade 4
ISBN: 978-0-85736-258-2

Vocals Grade 5
ISBN: 978-0-85736-259-9

Vocals Grade 6 (female voice)
ISBN: 978-0-85736-263-6

Vocals Grade 6 (male voice)
ISBN: 978-0-85736-260-5

Vocals Grade 7 (female voice)
ISBN: 978-0-85736-264-3

Vocals Grade 7 (male voice)
ISBN: 978-0-85736-261-2

Vocals Grade 8 (female voice)
ISBN: 978-0-85736-265-0

Vocals Grade 8 (male voice)
ISBN: 978-0-85736-262-9